# BABY'S FIRST YEAR

Written and devised by Christine L. Swift
Designed by Susan Bartram

© 1998 Grandreams Limited

Published by
**Grandreams Limited**
435-437 Edgware Road
Little Venice, London W2 1TH

Manufactured in China.

# Baby's Arrival

Date _____

Time _____

Place _____

Nurse _____

*Monday's child is fair of face*
*Tuesday's child is full of grace*
*Wednesday's child is full of woe*
*Thursday's child has far to go*
*Friday's child is loving and giving*
*Saturday's child works hard for a living*
*And the child that is born on the Sabbath day*
*Is bonny, blythe, good and gay*

# Baby's Appearance

*You probably spend a great deal of time looking at your baby and may already notice family resemblances. However, many things in your baby's appearance will gradually change during the course of the next few months.*
*Be sure to record these changes in the photograph sections provided.*

**Colour of eyes** (at birth) _____ (at 6 months) _____

**Colour of hair** (at birth) _____ (at 6 months) _____

**Complexion** (at birth) _____ (at 6 months) _____

**Weight** (at birth) _____ (at 6 months) _____

**Length** (at birth) _____ (at 6 months) _____

**Circumference of head** (at birth) _____ (at 6 months) _____

# First Photograph

*Baby's first photograph could even be a scan photograph taken before the baby was born or a photograph taken moments after the birth. Whenever this photograph was taken, it will always hold special memories of your baby in those very early days.*

**Birth sign** _____

**Birthstone** _____

## Visitors

_____
_____
_____
_____

## Gifts and flowers _____

_____
_____
_____
_____

## Cards _____

_____
_____
_____
_____

# Coming home

*There will be many things about the homecoming which you will always wish to remember. Maybe you've just decorated baby's room! Record these treasured moments here in photographs.*

*God bless this house from roof to floor*
*The twelve apostles guard the door*
*Four angels to my bed;*
*Gabriel stands at the head*
*John and Peter at my feet*
*All to watch me while I sleep.*

# Photographs

# Family Tree

Grandfather

_____

Grandfather

_____

Grandmother

_____

Grandmother

_____

Aunts

_____

_____

Aunts

_____

_____

Uncles

_____

_____

Uncles

_____

_____

Mother

_____

Father

_____

Brothers

_____

_____

Baby

_____

Sisters

_____

_____

## I was named

_____

On the _____ day of _____

At _____

In the presence of _____

_____

_____

_____

**My name means** _____

*Photograph*

# Hand prints  *Date:*

*Left-hand*　　　　　　　　　*Right-hand*

# Footprints  *Date:*

*Left-foot*　　　　　　　　　*Right-foot*

# Lock of hair

*First haircut:* _____

*Place:* _____

*Hairdresser:* _____

# Photographs

# Baby's Progress

*How many miles to babyland?*
*Anyone can tell;*
*Up one flight and to your right;*
*Don't forget to ring the bell.*

*First smile* _____

*First laugh* _____

*First rolled over* _____

*First slept through the night* _____

*First went into big bath* _____

*First slept in big cot* _____

First ate solid food _____

First tooth _____

First sat up _____

First crawled _____

First stood alone _____

First steps _____

First word _____

*What do they do in babyland?*
*They dream and wake and play;*
*They laugh and crow and fonder grow.*
*Jolly times have they.*

# Funny things I did

*As you watch your baby grow, there will be many little things which will amuse you. Use this space to record just some of these funny moments.*

# Naughty things I did

*With the best will in the world, a baby's curiosity will eventually get the better of him or her and there will be many naughty (but probably funny!) tales to tell.*

# Outings and visits

*Family and friends will all want to meet your new baby, so outings and visits are sure to play a major part of the early days. Record here those favourite occasions in visiting special friends, family and places. You may also wish to remember your baby's first holiday here.*

# Photographs

# My First Christmas

*Photograph*

*Where we spent it...*

_____

*Who with...*

_____

*Presents received...*

_____

_____

# Photographs

# My First Birthday

*The party was at...*